To Ed
From Bob
With affection
9/8/86

MUSIC AND MEDICINE

MUSIC AND MEDICINE

DESMOND O'SHAUGHNESSY

M.B.B.S., B.Sc. (Melb.)

F.R.C.S. (Edin.), F.R.A.C.S., D.Obst.R.C.O.G.

PRIVATELY PRINTED

This cover shows details from A Schubert Evening
in the Home of Josef von Spaun

Drawing by Moritz von Schwind;
original in the Schubert Museum

Reproduced by courtesy of the Archives of the
Austrian National Library

First published 1984

Printed in Australia by
Globe Press Pty Ltd, Brunswick, Victoria

ISBN 0 9591837 0 1

CONTENTS

INTRODUCTION

To many observers in quite a few of our contemporary hospitals the main connection between medicine and music might be thought to consist in that amorphous effluvium of mixed sound, sometimes even containing degraded threads of classical masterpieces, piped into the operating theatre to distract, annoy or perhaps please the surgeon and other personnel there. It has been said that the people who usually pay attention to such a salad of notes—and who soon seek their cessation—are those who love music. Silence, it need never be forgotten, is also music. This was stressed by Mozart and more recently by Yehudi Menuhin, who asserted it as one of the basic human rights.

Researching the various connections between medicine and music brings to light several kinds of associations. After all, virtually everyone comes into some sort of contact with doctors during life. Some of these contacts are basically professional, with the musician in the role of patient. In other circumstances, quite close friendships have developed between composers and doctors, with even inspiring and critical influences on creative writing.

These associations have fascinated me in particular since my student days, when I helped to pay for my medical course by writing the concert notices and a 600-word weekly article for the Saturday magazine pages of the Melbourne daily newspaper, the *Argus*. This also happened to be at one of those peaks of musical efflorescence in Australia, virtually at a turning point at the end of one era and the birth of another.

Some of Europe's great concert halls and opera houses were still in ruins or in the process of rebuilding. Freedom of travel had largely resumed and concert artists, many of them then far from rich, were glad of the opportunity of a visit to the Antipodes. Australia, after having been cut off in cultural isolation, welcomed them warmly and savoured their music to the full. There was a genuine excitement to be able to hear, as well as see, musicians who had been known for nearly a decade only by recordings and radio.

In the space of only about twelve months in 1938-39, just before the Second World War broke out, I had the unforgettable good fortune to hear in Melbourne Richard Tauber sing Mozart; Lotte Lehmann's interpretations of Schubert and Schumann; Kirsten Flagstad sing Grieg; and Artur Schnabel play the piano works of Beethoven and Schubert.

Among these early post-war visitors were several great artists of the past, whose careers were approaching their autumn but who still compensated for this by the authority and tradition of their interpretations. They had with them the culture that peaked in Europe between the two world wars: that unique interpreter of Debussy and Mozart, the pianist Walter Gieseking; Ninon Vallin, the exquisite singer of French art songs; and two great Russian pianists identified with the expansiveness and breadth of instrumental tradition in that country just after the turn of the century, Simon Barere and Benno Moiseiwitsch.

Then there were those who were virtually at their top and who, within the space of the next few years were to enjoy again the applause of the world: the Menuhins—Hephzibah was living in Victoria at that time—Rafael Kubelik, Eileen Joyce, Erna Berger, Witold Malcuzynski. During those days I grew to know Sophie Wyss, who sang the first performance of Benjamin Britten's 'Les Illuminations' and who championed modern music, such as that of the then relatively unknown Pierre Boulez (I am speaking of 1949). Mrs Louise

Dyer, the founder of the French Lyre-Bird Press, came back to her home city of Melbourne on a visit in 1947 and made me a farewell present of several recordings, left with a card inscribed: 'Because you love music'.

Eugene Goossens was resident conductor of the Sydney Symphony Orchestra and was bringing it to a high standard. Elisabeth Schwarzkopf, then relatively unknown outside Germany, gave us five lieder recitals; and sang in the last movement of the Fourth Symphony of Gustav Mahler. The latter was conducted by Otto Klemperer, who was also, I venture to say, at his best, probably even better than in those later years when London still justifiably lionized him. I would think that, of all visiting artists, he was the one I grew to know best personally. At that time, he was still somewhat uncertain in his gait and I treasure memories of holding his arm to negotiate his way through the bustling, lunch-hour crowds of Castlereagh Street, Sydney, after a rehearsal for the first Australian performance of the Ninth Symphony of Shostakovitch in 1949. Following his last concert in Melbourne, I relished the joy of being served with coffee and poppyseed strudel by his loving wife—he used to tease her affectionately and call her his 'Thirty Years' War'—while he sat up in bed, smoking his pipe and joking. Our final time together was after he conducted the Resurrection Symphony of Mahler in Sydney and I was invited by a doctor friend to supper at his home at Double Bay. The atmosphere breathed Salzburg of the early 1930s; a huge, green chestnut tree in the garden was bathed in moonlight; and Klemperer, jovial from good wine and food, entertained us all by singing the last movement of the Beethoven Ninth Symphony in Hungarian. (He had been conductor of the Budapest Opera House in the immediate postwar years.)

Other great concert performances included those of the Boyd Neel orchestra, who gave sixteen programmes in Melbourne; the Chopin and Rachmaninov Third Piano Concerto of William Kapell; and the Sibelius Violin Concerto of Ginette

Neveu. The latter died young and tragically in air crashes, while Boyd Neel, also a doctor, died late in 1981.

Interwoven with all this was the cultural stimulus provided by the English music critic, Neville Cardus, with his writings and weekly broadcasts on music. He came to live in Sydney in 1940 and stayed there for the next decade. I had the great pleasure of knowing him as friend, teacher and adviser. Here, again, memory recalls some wonderful anecdotes, conversations, company.

1
MYTHOLOGY TO BAROQUE

The earliest associations between medicine and music might be said to have been those of the Sun God, Apollo, the Greek god of music, poetry, dancing and healing: a temple built in his honour in Rome in 430 B.C. bore the dedication 'To Apollo Medicus Salutaris', the god of health. Although Apollo is usually pictured with his lyre, we must not forget that it is his name which is invoked in the Hippocratic oath: 'I swear by Apollo, the Physician, by Aesculapius, by Hygeia and Panacea and by all the gods and goddesses that, to the best of my power and judgement, I will faithfully observe this oath and obligation'.

Apollo was the father of Aesculapius, the god of healing, and had as his companions Terpsichore, the muse of choral dance and song; Polyhymnia, the muse of hymns; and Euterpe, the muse of lyric poetry. Legend has it that Aesculapius was reared by Chiron, famed for both his surgical skill and for his musical accomplishments.

Pythagoras regarded music and diet as the correct therapy to restore balance between mind and body; and Aristotle spoke of music as a release for pent-up emotions.

Tradition tells us that St Luke, the evangelist of the third Gospel, was not only a physician and painter but also the first Christian hymnologist: it is said that he wrote five of the first hymns of the early Church.

The Church during the Middle Ages, particularly in the big Benedictine and Augustinian monasteries, played a vital role in the development of Gregorian music; and also provided the hospitals and dispensaries of Europe. English legacies of this include St Thomas's and St Bartholomew's hospitals in London.

That early pharmacologist and late mediaeval practitioner of therapeutics, Paracelsus (1493–1541), began his career as an organist with successive appointments in Nuremburg, Innsbruck and Salzburg. He studied medicine at the University of Basle, where he returned to teach in 1526, preceding each lecture with a solemn burning of the works of Galen and Avicenna. He had to leave three years later, however, as his opponents pointed out that he had no degree. His pharmacology centred largely around minerals and alcoholic tinctures, but his medicine was based on superficial observations and superstitions. He taught that illness was due to a lack of 'Archaeus', an occult vital force situated in the stomach, where it separated the useful from the poisonous functions of the body.

Dr Felix Platter (1536–1614) was an accomplished player of the lute and his collection of musical instruments is still kept in Basle.

In England the Elizabethan poet, Thomas Campion (1567–1620), after studying law at Gray's Inn, turned to medicine at the age of thirty-five. He wrote a musical treatise in addition, a 'New Way of making Four Parts in Counterpoint by a most familiar and infallible rule'.

Athanasius Kircher (1602–80), the Jesuit from the ancient German city of Fulda, must have been one of those great Baroque all-rounders: a physician, mathematician, optician, orientalist, microscopist and musicologist. In addition to writing the text of *La Chine illustrée*, printed in Amsterdam in 1670, he wrote a 1200-page work, his *Mesurgia Universalis sive Ars magna consoni et dissoni*. It contains chapters on harmony, chromatics and rhythm, as well as ones on the anatomy and physiology of the ear and throat. It even includes a description of a composing machine; Samuel Pepys had one of them. The *Mesurgia* was published in Rome in 1637 and was considered to have collected all that was then known

2

of musical notations, of the songs of birds and the sounds of animals.

Dr Jan Arbuthnot (1667–1735), the English physician and friend of the poet Alexander Pope, was also a composer of religious music, his sacred anthem, 'As pants the hart', is still preserved in the collection at the Chapel Royal.

Caspar Secundus Bartholinus (1655–1738), medically remembered because of 'his' gland and cyst, published a paper, *De Tibiis Veterum,*, with details of the construction of the double flute of Ancient Greece and more recent instruments such as the basset and English horns, the oboe and the clarinet. (The original word '*tibia*' referred to a musical pipe or flute made out of bone, in addition to being the name of the bone of the shin.)

The French composer, Marin Marais (1656–1728) is respected in musical circles for his school of string playing and development of string ensemble during the reign of Louis XIV. His best-known opus is probably 'La Sonnerie de Ste Genevieve du Mont à Paris' but, to the medical profession, his noteworthiness rests on one work, his Tableau of a Bladder operation, a graphic description by bass viol, harpsichord and continuo of the various stages of a lithotomy: aspects of the surgical apparatus, the patient quails as he beholds it; he mounts the operating scaffold; seized with panic he thinks of fleeing; he reconsidereth; he is bound with cords of silk; the surgeon maketh his incision; the forceps is introduced; hereupon the stone is brought forth; here as it were the voice faileth; the blood, it floweth; the surgeon unloosens the silken cords; and now thou art put to bed; relief and rejoicing. The general merrymaking of the instruments in the finale breathes well-felt sighs of relief and joy.

TWO GREAT HOSPITAL BENEFACTORS: VIVALDI AND HANDEL

Il Prete rosso, Antonio Vivaldi (1678-1741) was not a doctor but *maestro di capella* on the staff of the Pieta, one of the four charitable Ospedali in Venice, where Italian string-playing probably made its greatest leap forward in form and technique.

The Ospedali were institutions for girls conducted by nuns and founded to house illegitimate, abandoned and orphaned children. Here they received a general education with a strong accent on music—so much so that the young ladies were often known only by their Christian names and instruments, such as Lucietta della viola, Luciana organista, Silvia dal violino, etc.

They were schooled in choral music and in instrumental ensemble with considerable attention to technique. It was this training, together with their spirit of teamwork, that helped Venetian composers forge that galaxy of string sinfonias, sonatas, concerti, masses, oratorios and other Church music that fill us still today with admiration for their opulence of sound and abundance. Vivaldi, for instance, wrote four hundred concerti for strings, featuring the various instruments in solo and group combinations and encircling the orchestral colour even further with cembalo, mandolin, oboe, flute and tympani. We see this, for instance, in works of his such as 'La Caccia', 'Il Favorito', 'La Stravaganza' and 'The Four Seasons'.

In the early eighteenth century Chiaretta of the Pieta and Anna Maria of the Ospedaletto were considered with Tartini to be the best violinists in Italy. The Ospedale degli Incurabili at one stage had as its maestro another great string composer, Baldassare Galuppi (1706–85).

The Church of Vivaldi's Ospedale, that of S. Maria di Pieta, has an oval ceiling with a Tiepolo fresco, 'The Triumph of the Blessed Virgin Mary', with the Madonna surrounded by an orchestra of various instruments. It still stands on the Riva degli Schiavoni, a short walk down from San Marco. Like all of them, the Ospedale di Pieta also had its staff physician,

'Gala Concert' by Guardi: with such a group as the girls from the Ospedale di Pieta under Vivaldi
From the Bavarian State Collection in the Alte Pinakothek Gallery, Munich

who visited it regularly: in Vivaldi's time he was Dr Domenico Bozzato.

One of the great Venetian attractions at carnival time and on Sundays and feast days was the series of concerts presented by these various ospedali. Their fame extended over virtually all Europe and among their recorded guests were the eminent English musicologist, Dr Burney; King Frederick IV of Denmark and Norway; and the Grand Duke Paul and the Grand Duchess Maria Feodorovna of Russia in 1782. Handel visited Venice and heard these concerts on at least two occasions, in 1707 and 1729. The painter, Francesco Guardi, has left us a very famous picture of one of them; but they also feature in the works of other artists such as Pietro Longhi and Gabriele Bella.

In England, the year 1685 saw the death of Charles II and the ascent of James II. On the continent of Europe 1685 was the year of the birth of no fewer than three great composers: George Frederick Handel on 23 February; Johann Sebastian Bach on 21 March; and Domenico Scarlatti on 26 October.

Handel's father in the German city of Halle was surgeon to the Duke of Sachsen-Weissenfels; and later expanded his business interests by obtaining permission from the Elector to purchase the inn, 'Zum gelben Hirsch', 'The Golden Stag'. Biography does not give us details of the operation which he performed on Andreas Rudolff, the Halle sword-swallower; details have to be left to our imaginations.

Whether or not Handel's *genu varum*, or bowed legs, which characterized his adult gait were due to a vitamin deficiency in childhood remains open to question. Perhaps it was just the result of chronic osteoarthritis brought on by his obesity.

When Handel went over to the Georgian beauty of Dublin in 1741 to present the first performance of 'The Messiah' at Neal's Musick Hall in Fishamble Street on 13 April the following year, among the charities sharing the £400 that was collected were the Charitable Infirmary of Dublin

Neal's music hall, Dublin, where the first performance of Handel's
'Messiah' was given
By courtesy of the Director of the National Library of Ireland, Dublin

and Mercer's Hospital. They both received £127. However,
Handel's meeting during this visit with another renowned
doctor did not have a medical connection, for that doctor was
the famed Dean of St Patrick's Cathedral, Dublin, Dr Dean
Swift.

On his return to London, Handel became very interested
in Captain Coram's Foundling Hospital, the Hospital for the
Maintenance and Education of Exposed and Deserted Young
Children. One of the aims of the institution was to combat
'gin, which reduced women to depravity and their unwanted

offspring to the dubious hospitality of the pavement'. An even stronger picture of the tragic social conditions of the day is the etched description of the admission-officer: 'Could he not realize the poignancy of waiting, while a woman ballotted with balls out of a bag as to whether the child should be admitted; or thrown back upon the world'.

The building still stands between the Hospital for Sick Children in Great Ormond Street and London House. Handel became one of its Governors (another one was the artist Hogarth). It was in aid of this Foundation that he offered a performance of 'The Royal Fireworks Music'.

In 1750 Handel presented the Foundling Hospital with an organ and played on it himself during a performance of 'The Messiah'. From that year onwards, he presided annually at the hospital 'Messiah', thus enriching it, according to Dr Burney, to the extent of nearly £7000. He also bequeathed to it parts of the score of the oratorio.

When a coat of arms was granted to the hospital in 1749 it included those of Halle, the composer's birthplace. It was in 1751, after one of these performances of 'The Messiah', that Handel first sought medical attention for his failing eyesight by consulting Dr Samuel Sharp, regarded as one of the first great surgeons of Guy's Hospital, London. He operated, alas without success and after total blindness had set in—it was even rumoured then that Handel was composing his own funeral anthem to be sung in the chapel of the Foundling Hospital. Further disappointing surgery was carried out by the itinerant optometrist, Chevalier John Taylor. The latter had travelled in Germany and operated on Johann Sebastian Bach in Leipzig in 1750, also unsuccessfully. During his long post-operative confinement in a darkened room, the elderly Bach became depressed by what he termed the *'schädliche Medikamente und Nebendinge'*, the drugs and dressings.

Handel died childless on 14 April 1759 at the age of 74. Johann Sebastian Bach died, after having sired twenty children, on 28 July 1750 at the age of 65 and only four months after his eye operation.

3
HAYDN AND MOZART

Joseph Haydn (1732–1809), the 'Father of the Symphony', was acquainted with the eminent surgeon, John Hunter, and his wife as a result of his visits to England. He set to music several of Mrs Hunter's poems, the most famous of which was the canzonet, 'My Mother bids me bind my hair'. It is also thought that she could have been the original librettist of his oratorio, 'The Creation', before it was translated into German by van Swieten.

John Hunter is recorded as having forcibly attempted to remove a nasal polyp from Haydn. That his love of composers was not as great as that of his wife may be gleaned from the following anecdote:

> On returning late one evening, after a hard day's fag, Hunter unexpectedly found his drawing-room filled with musical professors, connoisseurs and other idlers, whom Mrs Hunter had assembled. He was greatly irritated and walked straight into the room, addressed the astonished guests much in the following strain: 'I knew not of this kick-up and I ought to have been informed of it beforehand; but as I am now returned home to study, I hope the present company will retire'.

His instructions were promptly obeyed.

Haydn's last composition before his final departure from England in August 1795 was a setting of another of Mrs Hunter's verses: 'Oh, Tuneful Voice'.

Oliver Goldsmith (1728–74), the Irish author of *The Vicar of Wakefield*, employed his talents as an amateur musician on his way across the Continent on foot to study medicine in Padua.

'With one spare shirt, a flute and a single guinea', he 'turned what was my amusement into a pleasant means of subsistence'. According to his own accounts, his performances were appreciated more by the peasantry than by the nobility, as evidenced by his remark, 'but in truth, I am a stone, whenever I attempt to entertain persons of higher rank, they always thought my performance odious and never made me any return for my endeavours to please them'.

Edward Jenner (1749–1823), the father of modern vaccination, was an amateur violinist and flautist.

Dr Anton Mesmer, whose alleged hypnotic powers gave rise to a new word in the language, commissioned Wolfgang Amadeus Mozart to compose the short operetta, 'Bastien and Bastienne'. The little opera was first performed in the garden theatre of Mesmer's home in the Landstrasse district of Vienna and I can remember seeing it staged in the Melbourne Town Hall by the Mozart Boys Choir of Vienna under De Georg Gruber in 1939 a few months before the outbreak of war. One of the interesting features of the work is the similarity between its opening theme and the introduction of the 'Eroica' Symphony of Beethoven.

Leopold Auenbrugger (1772–1809), medically known as the founder of the art of percussion of the chest and abdomen, drew his inspiration from noticing how his father, a vintner, used this method to estimate the state of emptiness or fullness of his wine barrels. He also gave his name to Auenbrugger's sign, a bulging of the epigastrium in diffuse pericardial effusion. His other claim to fame is that he wrote the libretto to Salieri's opera *'Der Rauchfangkehrer'*, 'The Chimney Sweep'. Salieri, who was Second Court Capellmeister to the Austrian Emperor, Joseph II, recommended the appointment of Lorenzo da Ponte as poet to the court theatre; but it would seem that there was some animosity between him and Mozart. On the other hand, he was one of the teachers of Schubert and exhibited his pride after the successful performance of the Mass in F at the Lichtenthal Church in Vienna. When Salieri died in 1826, Schubert made an unsuccessful application to the then Emperor, Francis II, to be appointed his successor.

Wolfgang Amadeus Mozart (1756–91)

The tragedy of the final illness, strange death and anonymous burial have long intrigued biographers. More recently, there has arisen the theory that his death was from renal failure, resulting from poisoning by mercury administered by Salieri. On the other hand, it is possible that the oedema was part of a terminal episode of rheumatic carditis, endocarditis and atrial fibrillation.

During those extensive and undoubtedly very uncomfortable travels with his children over most of Europe, the composer's father Leopold took with him what must have been virtually a small portable dispensary. The ingredients of two of his favourite mixtures merit recording as medical curiosities: Magrafenpulver included magnesium carbonate, peony and iris roots, mistletoe, crushed coral and gold; while the main constituents of Schwarzpulver were charcoal, deers' antlers, myrrh, coral, earthworms, frogs' heads and placenta.

4
LUDWIG VAN BEETHOVEN (1770–1827)

Even before he left Bonn, the Rhineland city of his birth, a close medical friendship had already sprung up between Beethoven and the young Dr Franz Wegeler. They had met at the home of the von Breuning family, one of the daughters of whom, Eleonore von Breuning, Wegeler later married. After Beethoven went to live in Vienna in 1792, they still corresponded and some of their letters provide one of the best written sources of information on the composer's deafness and ill-health in general.

It is recorded that Beethoven contracted a rather severe respiratory tract infection badly affecting his hearing in 1796, when he came back to his room in Vienna on a very warm summer's day, stripped to the waist and cooled himself in a draught of air at the window. Some authorities have suggested that what followed was an attack of typhoid fever but I wonder if it could have been an acute otitis media, complicated in turn by a perforation of the eardrum? In any case, his hearing deteriorated noticeably afterwards. In 1798 he wrote to a friend: 'I must tell you that my most noble part, my ear, has begun to fail badly'. In the same letter, he complained of recurrent diarrhoea and spoke of this again in a further letter of 1801.

It was also in 1801 that Beethoven wrote to Dr Wegeler of having consulted the Director of the General Hospital in Vienna, Dr Frank (whose home towards the end of that century became that of Billroth). The instillations of almond oil which were recommended proved of no help for the '*Sausen und Brausen*', the continuous buzzing in his ears day and night, as well as the loss of hearing for higher tones. Beethoven said that he could then still hear the lower ones in conversation; and added that his bowel problems had become worse. In another letter to Wegeler in that same year, 1801, the composer said that he thought that the ringing in his ears might have diminished; but his hearing, especially in his left ear, was no better. He sought his medical friend's advice on the possible curative effects of Galvanism, citing two reported cures of deafness in Berlin using this method.

By 1802 Beethoven's depression over his affliction had deepened further, as evidenced by the famous Heiligenstadt Testament. While he was staying in that outer part of Vienna, he also composed his Second Symphony.

The 'Eroica' Symphony, No. 3 in E Flat Major, was published in 1804; and the Fifth and Sixth Symphonies were completed at Heiligenstadt in 1808. In 1809 he composed the 'Emperor' Concerto, as well as the Opus 81a piano sonata, '*Les Adieux*', dedicated to his friend, the Archduke Rudolf. It was also in that year that Beethoven had to seek refuge in a cellar, covering his head with pillows to dull the pain in his ears caused by the reverberations of the bombardment of the city by Napoleon's troops.

A further reference to his deafness is contained in a letter of 1810 to Wegeler: 'Still I should not only be happy but the happiest of men, if a demon had not taken up his settled abode in my ears'. Ludwig Spohr, a composer contemporary with Beethoven, visited him in 1812 and again in 1814 and reported that the deafness was so severe that, in order to make himself understood, he had to shout so loudly that he could be heard three rooms away. When Beethoven sat down to play the piano for him, it was out of tune. He hit the keys so forcibly in the forte passages that the strings twanged, while many of the softer ones were virtually inaudible.

The use of an ear-trumpet fixed by a headband and made by Johann Malzel in 1814 proved a failure. The biographer,

Schindler, recorded that conversation was practically impossible after about that time; and it was in the same period that Beethoven started his famous conversation-notebooks. Their number was first thought to have reached 188, but another authority gives a higher figure in the region of 400 and has stated that 260 were destroyed in the nineteenth century because they were thought to be of 'no value'.

A serious episode of diarrhoea struck in 1812 and in 1821 he suffered from a severe jaundice. In February 1822 he complained of a particularly bad attack of otalgia, earache; but he made no reference to any ear discharge. An especially touching illustration of the sufferings brought about by his deafness is the story, that when he stood up to acknowledge the applause after the first performance of his Ninth (Choral) Symphony in 1824, he did so with his back to the cheering crowd; and had to be turned around by one of the singers.

In 1825 he wrote to Dr Braunhofer that he had had repeated bleedings from his nose and had coughed up blood on one occasion over a period of several months. Was there some irony behind his setting to music later that same day the words:

Doktor sperrt das Thor dem Tod
Note hilft auch aus der Noth?
(Doctor close the door against Death,
Notes will also help in need.)

It was after he had recovered from the illness treated by Dr Braunhofer, however, that Beethoven wrote the A Minor, Opus 132, Quartet with the movement, *'Heiliger Dankgesang eines Genesenen an die Gottheit in der lydischen Tonart'*, the sacred song of thanksgiving in the Lydian mode to the Godhead from one healed of sickness.

Late in 1826 and in the early part of 1827 the jaundice returned, complicated by the development of gross ascites. Eleven litres of fluid were aspirated from his abdominal

Beethoven's funeral procession, 29 March 1827
Designed by von Kuhler; lithograph by Franz Stöber
From the Vienna State Museum

cavity on the first occasion; and the second paracentesis yielded twenty litres.

In his last illness Beethoven was attended by Dr Malfatti, to whose allegedly frivolous niece he is said to have once proposed marriage. Perceiving the hopelessness of the situation medically, Dr Malfatti discontinued all medication, substituting for it some iced punch for the high fever.

Beethoven died on 26 March 1827 at the age of 57. The immediate cause of death was said to have been broncho-pneumonia. Two days later an extensive autopsy was performed by Dr Johann Wagner of the Pathological Museum of Vienna, assisted by Dr Carl von Rokitansky. (The latter's staining method is still used in one of the preparations of microscope slides by pathologists.)

Their main findings comprised: a shrunken cirrhotic liver; an abdominal ascites of eight litres of fluid; wasted limbs; 'glistening cutaneous scales lining the external auditory canal, especially around the drum; a very thickened Eustachian tube with scarred depressions near its pharangeal opening; large cellular mastoid; facial nerves of considerable thickness, shrunken auditory nerves, a softer brain than normal due to increased fluid content; and a dense vascular pia-arachnoid around the fourth ventricle and brain-stem'.

It is my private opinion that the cause of Beethoven's many attacks of diarrhoea over so many years was chronic ulcerative colitis; and that this was later complicated by the development of biliary cirrhosis of the liver, giving rise to the ascites. The true cause of his chronic deafness, I strongly believe, still remains an open, unsolved question.

An Ann Arbor (Michigan) authority on ear, nose and throat conditions suggests that it was syphilitic. This is possible but there are features which still raise doubts. With such limited post-mortem information, I wonder whether we can even be certain that Beethoven suffered from a hydrops of his inner ears? And, if he did, there are other causes of it besides syphilis, such as high blood pressure or emotion. Furthermore, just because there are no reports of chronic ear discharges, it does not necessarily follow that he could not have had chronic perforations of both drums brought on by acute otitis media.

Otosclerosis, fixation of the footplate of the stapes, would be characterized rather by a mid-tone loss of hearing and could explain reports that Beethoven used a bone-conduction aid, a drumstick, *baguette de bois*, between his teeth to hear the piano when he was composing in later years.

Against the diagnosis of otosclerosis would be the atrophy of the auditory nerve. This atrophy raises the possibility of yet another explanation, namely Paget's Disease, perhaps even localized to the skull. Sir James Paget did not describe the disease until 1877, fifty years after Beethoven's death; and the oft-quoted saying that one of the initial symptoms of such a patient may be the complaint of having to take increasingly larger sizes in hats, may be pertinent to the composer's physiognomy. From drawings, Beethoven had a very prominent forehead and used to wear his hat on the back of his head. Against the suggested diagnosis of Paget's Disease would be the early age of onset of his deafness; but another feature in favour of it could be that he lost first the high ranges of tone. A strong supporting finding would be the reduced size of the auditory nerve at post-mortem: Paget's Disease is characterized by narrowing of the internal auditory meatus in the temporal bones of the skull.

However, Beethoven's temporal bones have been lost! They were removed for further study by the pathologist, Dr Wagner, and have disappeared from the Vienna Anatomy Institute. There have been two exhumations, in 1863 and 1884. This also means that it is impossible to study the three little ossicles of the middle ear, including the stapes.

One factor lending suspicion to the syphilitic theory would be the report that Beethoven's friend, Dr Bertolini, spoke of guarding two confidential prescriptions for treatment of some illness and, although their friendship broke up in 1815, that medical confidence was still respected. Among other things, I find it hard to suspect Beethoven of syphilis just because of his being virtually never 'out of love' and to have yearned for various young ladies. Can it be assumed that such reveries found full physical fulfilment? The opposite might well be the explanation?

Inconsistencies are found in practically everyone; but the belief that Beethoven led what might be termed an old-fashioned virtuous life could at least be supported by his disapproval of the plots of two of Mozart's operas, those of 'Cosi fan Tutte' and 'The Marriage of Figaro'. Added to this was his eagerness to make his only opera, 'Fidelio', a tribute to the strength of marriage. Schindler, probably the first important biographer of Beethoven, said of him that he spent his life in virginal modesty without having to reproach himself in any way.

A Schubert evening in a Viennese home; *oil painting on canvas by Julius Schmid*
Museum of the City of Vienna

5
FRANZ SCHUBERT

There are only a few slender medical connections in the life of Franz Schubert (1797–1828).

During 1818, the year he spent at Castle Zseilz, the country residence of Count Johann Esterhazy as tutor to his two daughters, the composer wrote that his favourite member of the household was the doctor: 'The surgeon, whom I like best, is a venerable old man of 75, always cheerful and happy. May God give everyone so happy an old age!' Back in Vienna, one of the peripheral members of the Schubertiad circle included a surgeon, Dr Menz.

We do not know the name of the doctor who attended Schubert in his last days, when he died of typhoid fever at the age of only 31—and after having left the world more than 600 songs, 9 symphonies, 20 string quartets, a string quintet, as well as waltzes, overtures, church music and choral works.

6
CHOPIN AND TUBERCULOSIS

In view of his long struggle against chronic pulmonary tuberculosis, it is not surprising to learn that Frederic Chopin (1810–49) had at least intermittent connections with doctors.

The first of these, however, was one of friendship. After finally leaving Poland in 1830, he travelled to Vienna where he developed an illness described as a prolonged attack of nasal catarrh. The doctor whom he consulted there, Dr Johann Malfatti, was the same one who had attended the dying Beethoven. Being also a great music-lover and having a Polish wife, it was not surprising that a firm friendship developed between the three: Mrs Malfatti loved to spoil the composer with Polish dishes when he came to dine at their home and, when Chopin went on to Paris, the most influential letter of introduction which he took was that from this doctor to the 60-year-old composer and conductor, Ferdinando Paer. The latter's recommendation was largely responsible for Chopin being given permission to settle in the French capital; and it was he who introduced him to Cherubini, Rossini, Mendelssohn and Kalkbrenner. The latter was a very important teacher at the Conservatoire and connected with the leading piano firm of Pleyel.

The existence of pulmonary tuberculosis became dramatically evident during Chopin's stay with the author, George Sand, in the damp, ruined Carthusian Monastery of Valldemosa near Palma on the island of Majorca in 1838–39. Even the local inhabitants had their suspicions and treated the pair as outcasts for this and moral reasons. By law, their bedding had to be later burned. As soon as they returned to France, Chopin was seen in Marseilles by Dr Francois Cauviere, who advised a month's rest for the haemoptyses. It proved effective but only temporarily.

At Nohant, George Sand's estate in the Province of Berry, Chopin came under the care of Dr Gustave Papet, the local doctor who had known the author since she was a child. He used to come over on horseback to visit his patient and gave as diagnosis an inflammation of the larynx. George Sand, however, was in no doubt as to the true nature of the disease and voiced this in a letter to the painter Delacroix, one of Chopin's best friends. The composer, nevertheless, had greater trust and wrote: 'Dear, dear doctor, thanks to you here I am on my legs and if you want me to jump, I'll try to fall on your neck in gratitude'.

Sand's passion cooled later and the breaking off of the physical relationship in 1843 was said to have been on the advice of Dr Papet. By mid-1849, by which time haemoptyses were virtually a daily event, Chopin's favourite Paris physician, Dr Molin, was dead; and his medical care was taken over by a series of physicians: Dr Louis, Dr Roth, Dr Simon, Dr Blache, Dr Fraenkel and finally by the most eminent of them all, Dr Jean Cruveilhier. He is best known in medical circles for having been one of the first to propound a theory on the development of diverticulitis of the colon; and it was he who attended Chopin on his deathbed in No. 12 Place Vendome. It is recorded how, several hours before the composer's death, he held a candle in front of his eyes and, finding no reaction, inquired if he was in pain. 'No more', was the enfeebled reply. George Sand is said to have been turned away from the door two days beforehand. Another of Chopin's loves, the Polish Countess Delphine Potocka sang a psalm by Marcello to him at his request in those last hours. He dedicated the Minute Waltz to her; and there is a painting of her as a Madonna in the Wallace Collection in London.

Anointed with the last rites of the Church, administered by the Polish chaplain, Father Jelowicki, Chopin died in his apartment in the Place Vendome—there is a small plaque commemorating it on the outside of the building below—at 2 a.m. on 17 October 1849.

Thirteen days later, on 30 October, the Grecian facade of the Church of the Madeleine was draped in black and under a black catafalque with the initials F.C. in silver on it, the coffin was brought in to the strains of the funeral march from his B Minor Sonata. At the composer's request, Mozart's Requiem was sung during the Mass, after which a long procession wended its way along the Paris boulevards to the grave in the Père Lachaise Cemetery. Chopin's heart was sent to Warsaw, where it rests there in the Church of the Holy Cross.

7

HECTOR BERLIOZ: MEDICAL STUDENT

Hector Berlioz (1803–69) was born in a small town between Grenoble and Lyons and was taught to play the flute and guitar by his father, Dr Louis Berlioz.

> My father intended me to follow his profession, which he considered to be the finest in the world. I, on my side made no secret of what I thought of it and my vigorous expressions of dissent on one or two occasions had not pleased him. I had a strong presentiment that my life was not going to be spent at the bedside of the sick, in hospitals and dissecting rooms.

In his efforts to interest his son in his profession, Dr Berlioz spread out in his study Munro's enormous treatise on anatomy, with life-sized illustrations of the structure of the body. As a further enticement, he offered to buy his son in Lyons a beautiful flute with all new keys, something which young Hector had coveted for a long time. But he still voiced his abhorrence over the prospects of a medical course:

> Become a doctor! study anatomy! dissect! take part in horrible operations—instead of giving myself body and soul to music, sublime art, whose grandeur I was beginning to perceive. Forsake the highest heaven for the wretchedest regions of earth; the immortal spirits of poetry and love and their divinely inspired strains for dirty hospital orderlies, dreadful dissecting-room attendants, hideous corpses, screams of patients, the groans and rattling breath of the dying. No! No!

Nevertheless, he began to study medicine with his cousin, Alphonse Robert, who later became a distinguished Paris doctor and who helped to teach him at the request of his father. Robert was also a fine violinist and much of their time which should have gone to the study of anatomy went towards music. However, Berlioz remarked that Robert always seemed to know far more about the demonstrations afterwards than he did.

His account of his medical studies continued:

Nevertheless, partly by my own efforts, partly by coercion, I managed after a fashion to learn all of the anatomy my father could teach me from prepared specimens (skeletons); and, encouraged by my fellow-students, I resolved to attack my medical studies in earnest and with that end to go with him to Paris. On arriving in Paris in 1822 with my fellow-student, Alphonse Robert, I gave myself up wholly to the study for the career which had been thrust on me; and loyally kept the promise I'd given my father on leaving.

It was soon put to a somewhat severe test when Robert, having announced one morning that he had bought a subject, i.e. a corpse, took me for the first time to the dissecting-room at the Hospice de la Pitié. At the sight of that terrible charnel-house—the fragments of limbs, the grinning heads and gaping skulls, the bloody quagmire underfoot and the atrocious smell it gave off, the swarms of sparrows wrangling over scraps of lung, the rats in their corner gnawing the bleeding vertebrae—such a feeling of revulsion possessed me that I leapt through the window of the dissecting-room; and fled for home as though death and all his hideous train were on my heels.

The shock of that first impression lasted for twenty-four hours. I did not want to hear another word about anatomy, dissecting or medicine and I meditated a hundred mad schemes to escape from the future that hung over me.

However, Robert eventually persuaded Berlioz to make a second attempt and then he found that the sights which had

* For quotations on pages 23–25 I am greatly indebted to Mr David Cairns' book on Berlioz published by Victor Gollancz.

horrified him the previous day were no longer so repulsive to him:

> I felt but a cold distaste; I was already as hardened to the scene as any seasoned medical student. The crisis was passed. I found that I actually enjoyed groping about in a poor fellow's chest and feeding the winged inhabitants of that delightful place with their ration of lung. 'Hello!', Robert cried laughing; 'you're getting civilised'.

Berlioz' retort to this was that he was giving the birds their meat in due season and, at that moment, he tossed a shoulder-blade over to a great rat that was staring at him with 'famished eyes'. (The physics lecturer at this time was the eminent Gay Lussac.)

Just when it looked as if he had finally settled down to becoming a good medical student, Berlioz took the fatal step of going to the Paris Opera. Here, he saw 'Les Danaides' of Salieri and was totally overwhelmed by the spectacle of the ballet, of the voice of the soprano, and the combined sound from the chorus and orchestra. Next day, he kept humming the main aria in the dissecting-room and his companions voiced their disapproval of the waste of time and of the money they had all used to purchase their cadaver.

Much later, in July 1827, Berlioz practised a little surgery on himself when he developed a quinsy and lanced his own retro-tonsillar abscess with a pen-knife! He became ill during a visit to Leipzig in 1843; and when he finally inquired from the local doctor about his attendance fee, he was told that the deal could be settled by his writing the theme of his Mass-Offertorium and attaching his signature to it.

Berlioz' infatuation with the Irish Shakespearian actress, Harriet Smithson, whom he first saw playing Ophelia in *Hamlet*, inspired his *Symphonie Fantastique*. The textures and fantasies interwoven in its introduction, the magic of the harp in the ballroom scene and the dreaminess evoked by the woodwind in the Pastorale create effects of hovering, romantic visions of his 'Immortal Beloved'. This, of course, intensifies the downward plunge of the march to the scaffold and her taking part in the witches' sabbath: the eeriness of the latter movement seems to draw on his memories of those grizzly days in the Paris dissecting-rooms. To have seen the role of the Immortal Beloved danced by Irina Baronova and Tamara Toumanova in the Russian companies of the late 1930s and early 1940s settles any arguments as to the suit-ability of this work to be presented as a symphonic ballet.

With such a powerful imagination, it is not surprising that Berlioz' orchestration does not follow the traditional line of many other composers. Some attribute his original instrumental colouring to the fact that he played the flute and the guitar but rarely resorted to the piano. However, two giants of the piano and great friends of his, Liszt and Chopin, took part in the same recital when a Benefit Concert was given to help Harriet, when she broke her leg and was in straitened circumstances. Just think of the musical feast that audience enjoyed!

With his strongly romantic nature, Berlioz enthused with almost reflex alacrity to the inspiration of Byron's *Childe Harold* and Shakespeare's *Romeo and Juliet*, delineating the former in the viola solo; and, in the case of the latter, musical colours shimmering in the atmospheric portrayal of the scene 'Romeo's Reverie at the Fete of the Capulets'. Other great works of his include the oratorio 'The Childhood of Christ'; the song cycle *'Nuits d'Eté'* (Summer Nights); and his operas on a grand scale, 'The Trojans' and 'The Damnation of Faust'.

Jacob Henle (1809–85), after whom a loop in the kidney is named, was regarded as an excellent violin and cello player in Zurich. He was also a personal friend of Mendelssohn.

Herman Ludwig Helmholtz (1821–94) was a mathematician, physicist, physiologist, medical man and music-lover. In the 1850s he made extensive studies on the basis of harmony and

A caricature of Berlioz as conductor of an eccentric giant orchestra; *a print from an engraving by Jean Isadore Gérard, called Grandville* From the archives of the Austrian National Library

dissonance, the theory of organ-pipes, musical temperatures, timbre (*Klangfarbe*), and the Arabian and Persian musical scales. His treatise on the physiological basis of tone sensations was regarded as a landmark and in 1863 he published his monumental work on tonal sensations, *Tonempfindungen.*

He must have possessed a very impressive appearance if one accepts the description of him given by Professor McKendrick of Glasgow; when the latter was at the Leipzig Gewandhaus Concerthall for a performance of Mendelssohn's 'Midsummer Night's Dream' in 1872, he said that he suspected that it was Helmholtz when he saw there 'a head of such splendid proportions with the eyes having a rapt expression' as the music floated through the hall. He was proved right a few days later when he visited him at his laboratory and there received advice concerning the ophthalmometer and some acoustic apparatus.

Dr Robert Dwyer Joyce (1830–83) received his first education at a hedge school in Ireland in the penal days; and later trained as a teacher, eventually becoming principal of Clonmel Model School. He resigned this position, however, in 1857 in order to study medicine at Queen's College, Cork. He helped to pay his fees by contributing poems, stories and articles to papers such as *The Nation*; and, in 1861, he published a book of ballads, romances and songs.

He graduated as a doctor in 1865 and, as Catholic Emancipation had extended by then to the foundation and opening of the National University of Ireland, became Professor of English Literature there. He later went to the United States, where he continued to write; and to lecture at the Harvard Medical School. In 1883, he came back to Dublin but died a few months later.

8
BILLROTH AND BRAHMS

Many would look on the friendship between the composer, Johannes Brahms and the pioneer of gastric surgery, Theodor Billroth, as being probably the closest personal association in the history of music and medicine.

Theodor Billroth was born of Swedish parents on the German island of Rügen in the Baltic Sea on 26 April 1829. As has been customary for a long time in Germany, he studied at several universities, namely those of Greifswald, Göttingen and finally Berlin, where he received his degree in 1852. Between 1853 and 1860 he was an Assistant at Langenbeck's Surgical Clinic in Berlin and was later given the title of Dozent, entitling him to lecture at the university. In 1860 Billroth became Professor of Surgery and Director of the Surgical Clinic of the University of Zürich; and it was here that his friendship with Brahms began. Billroth was appointed Professor of Surgery at the University of Vienna in 1867 and in his subsequent years there pioneered many paths, above all those involving resection of the stomach. Models of his operations are to be seen in a museum in Vienna and, when I was in that city some years ago looking for Schubert's birthplace, I was carried on too far by the tram. When I realized this, I alighted and, to my surprise, I saw a bust on an obelisk on the opposite side of the road. Recognizing it as that of Billroth and prompted by curiosity, I visited the hospital behind it and found that it had been endowed by the Archduke Rudolf, the eldest son of the Emperor Franz Joseph, the son who left his mark in romantic history in the tragedy of Mayerling. This was Billroth's private surgical clinic and there I was shown some diagrams of his operations, as well as several other relics.

Billroth's first complete surgical resection of the larynx was carried out in 1873, the same year in which Brahms dedicated to him the two string quartets, Op. 51. In 1881 Billroth excised from a stomach an ulcer which was thought to have been more likely malignant than peptic; and he sutured together the divided ends of the upper stomach and the duodenum, thus performing the first Billroth I operation of gastroduodenostomy. Four years later, in 1885, he resected a tumour from the antrum of the stomach, closing the cut ends of it and the duodenum; and performing an anterior gastrojejunostomy with diversion of the bile and pancreatic secretions. It is basically what is known as the Billroth II procedure with removal of most of the acid-secreting area of the stomach and the gastrin-secreting antrum.

The Billroth II operation is sometimes given the additional appellation of Polya; but the latter did not write his paper until 1911. An earlier one dealing with resection of the pylorus and gastroenterostomy was that of Kronlein in 1888.

Melbourne is very fortunate to have in its State Library several English translations of textbooks by Billroth, including his *Clinical Surgical Extracts, General Surgery and Pathology* and *The Medical Sciences in the German Universities.*

The 665-page volume entitled *General Surgical Pathology and Therapeutics in Fifty Lectures,* published by Thomas Lewis of Gower Street, London, in 1871 and translated by Charles E. Hackley of New York, begins with the following laudatory preface:

During the past ten years, the microscope has greatly advanced our knowledge of pathology; and it will perhaps be acknowledged that most progress in the study of pathological anatomy has been made in Germany. Professor Theodor Billroth, himself one of the most noted

30

Theodor Billroth in 1894 with a facsimile of his signature; *etching by Ludwig Michalele*
From the Archives of the Austrian National Library

authorities in surgical pathology, has in the present volume given us a complete resume of the existing state of knowledge in this branch of medical science.

Its chapters include the following titles: Simple Incised Wounds in the Soft Parts; Simple Fractures of Bones; Open Fractures and Suppuration of Bone; Injuries of the Joints;

Acute Inflammation of the Bones, Periosteum and Joints; Gangrene; Accidental Traumatic and Inflammatory Diseases and Poisoned Wounds; Ulcers; Chronic Inflammation of the Periosteum, of the Bone and Necrosis; Chronic Inflammation of the Joints; Varices and Aneurysms; and Tumours.

Billroth's introductory lecture began:

Gentlemen. The study of Surgery, which you began with this lecture is now, in most countries, justly regarded as a necessity for the practising physician. We consider it a happy advance that the division of surgery from medicine no longer exists as it did formerly. The difference between internal medicine and surgery is in fact only apparent; the distinction is artificial, founded though it be on history, and on the large and increasing literature of General Medicine.

In the course of this work, your attention will often be called to the frequency with which surgery must consider the general state of the body, to the analogy between the diseases of the external and the internal parts and to the fact that the whole difference depends on our seeing before us the changes of tissue that occur in surgical disease, while we have to determine the affections of intestinal organs from the symptoms . . .

In short, the surgeon can only judge safely and correctly the state of his patient when he is at the same time a physician . . .

The proper treatment of wounds is to be regarded as the most important requirement for the surgeon, not only on account of the frequency of this variety of injury but because we so often intentionally make them in operation, even when operating for something that is not itself danger to life. Hence, we are answerable for the healing of the wound, to as great an extent as it is possible by experience.

In large wounds we now avoid the use of adhesive plaster more than formerly and in its place employ the suture more commonly. When we wish to unite wounds by the suture, we generally choose between two varieties, the interrupted sutura nodosa and the twisted suture, the sutura circumvoluta. There is some truth in the assertion that, by the introduction of a foreign body such as a thread or needle, we maintain constant irritation in the edges of

Billroth in his lecture theatre; *art print, A. Seligmann, 1890*
From the State Museum, Vienna

the wound; but this cannot equal the great advantage obtained by the certainty of adjustment of the edges of the wound by means of sutures'.

In later chapters we read of: The Subcutaneous Osteotomy of

Baron von Langenbeck for obliquely united fractures; Pseudarthrosis; Phlegmonous Inflammation of the Cellular Tissues, i.e. Acute Cellulitis; Phlebitis, Thrombosis and Embolism—the latter causing the local ischaemia of Virchow; Osteomalacia; Contraction of the Palmar Fascia—those who work with hammer, axe; but Baron von Langenbeck mentions those who seal or stamp letters all day. In many persons with this disease—almost certainly Dupuytren's Contracture—no cause or connection with other disease is discoverable. Reference is also made to Hunter's Ligation of Aneurysms.

Billroth's Chapter on Carcinomata begins with perspective:

To give you an idea of how tumours were formerly diagnosed and of the origin of many of the names still in use, I will read you a passage from the classical and, in its time, most prominent work of Lorenz Heister, the third edition of which published in 1731, I have before me. Heister on p. 220 says: The name "scirrhus' is given to a painless tumour that occurs in all parts of the body but especially in the glands and is due to stagnation and drying of the blood in the hardened part. When a scirrhus is not reabsorbed, cannot be arrested or is not removed by time, it either spontaneously or from mal-treatment becomes malignant, that is painful and inflamed; and then we begin to call it cancer or carcinoma; at the same time the veins swell up and distend like the feet of a crab (but this does not happen in all cases) whence the disease gets its name; it is in fact one of the worst, most horrible and most painful of diseases. While the skin remains intact over it, it is termed hidden, (cancer occultus) but, when the skin has opened or ulcerated, it is called open or ulcerated cancer; the latter usually succeeds the former.

It is not long since man lived in the simple belief that there was something real and truly practical in this mode of comparison and description. In a hundred years, will they laugh at our present anatomical and clinical definitions, as we do now at good, old Heister? Who knows? Time moves on with great strides; things come to light and, before we have time to look around, they are

34

turned into history by careful labours of young experimenters.

The classical monographs of Astley Cooper on diseases of the testis and breast (the latter unfortunately unfinished), show that by a careful study of the points perceptible to the naked eye, a great deal may be obtained by studying a single organ.

In the stomach, gland-cancers are frequent, especially with mucous softening (gelatinous cancer) and cancer of the liver; cancer of the duodenum is very rare.

Unfortunately, the aetiology of cancer gives no clue to treatment; we know too little of the causes why certain tumours are so infectious, while others are not so. A blow, kick, etc. may occasionally induce an outbreak of the disease in some few cases but cannot excite the predisposition to cancer. In other cases, inheritance of the disease is evident. Care and anxiety may hasten the course of the disease but do not induce it.

We have now to criticise the caustics chiefly used in cancers.

In the course of time, opinions about caustics have differed greatly; at times they were greatly preferred to the knife, again they were entirely thrown aside. The views of most surgeons of the present day, as well as my own, incline to the latter one.

I decidedly prefer the operation with the knife or scissors, because I know exactly what I remove and I can judge more certainly if all the diseased part has been excised. Hence I regard the operative removal of cancer as well as of other tumours to be preferable as a rule. But where there is a rule, there are exceptions . . . In very old, anaemic or timid patients, caustics may be employed . . . for a caustic I prefer Chloride of Zinc to all others for destroying cancers: you may use it as a paste or as caustic arrows.

The following are extracts from another of his works: *Clinical Surgery*—Extracts from the Reports of Surgical Practice between the years 1860 and 1876 by Dr Theodor Billroth.

In the preface to this volume Mr C.T. Dent, F.R.C.S. of St George's Hospital, London, wrote in 1881:

The present method of conducting antiseptic operations in Professor Billroth's clinic is briefly as follows: No spray is used. Carbolic Acid is the antiseptic agent employed in solution of 1%, 3%, or 5%. The instruments and sponges (special care being taken with the latter) are rendered thoroughly aseptic. Silk ligatures are found to answer best; the threads are boiled for one hour in 5% solution of Carbolic Acid before use. The ends of the ligature are cut off close to the knot . . . the Lister's mackintosh is replaced by a special soft, impermeable material of less expensive nature. The dressings are, as a rule, changed for the first time on the fifth day. The drainage tubes are then removed and the second dressing allowed to remain on for five or six days, at the end of which period the special antiseptic precautions are usually discontinued. For the above information I am indebted chiefly to the courtesy of Dr Johann Mikulicz of Vienna, assistant in Professor Billroth's clinic.

Much of the volume is concerned with the antiseptic treatment of wounds, carrying out injunctions of Lister and Volkmann; Carbolic Acid poisoning; Pyaemia; Traumatic Erysipelas. There is a diagram showing a 4-5-inch-long incision running obliquely across the epigastrium not very far above the level of the umbilicus for exposure of the pylorus. The advice is for the surgeon not to go ahead if the growth is adherent to the pancreas or transverse colon, because of the high risk of resection proving fatal.

A description for removal of the greater omentum is given; and all blood vessels are to be tied off with fine antiseptic silk, 'the knotted ends left hanging for the time, so as to hold the stomach'.

In this description of the Billroth I Gastroduodenostomy, Billroth gives instructions for the incision to be carried obliquely though the stomach 'to avoid folds in sewing-up'. 'The lumen of the stomach should be so far closed by Lembert's sutures that the opening left is no larger than that of the duodenum.' With regard to post-operative care, Billroth's patients were allowed to receive a tablespoonful of cold sour milk on the day after the operation.

When Billroth came to Vienna in 1867, the Brahms–Wagner feud was increasing in temperature, the flames being

Johannes Brahms
Archives of the Austrian National Library

fanned by the pedantic music critic, Edward Hanslick, later to
be mocked and immortalized by Wagner in the character of
Beckmesser in his opera 'The Mastersingers of Nuremburg'.

As a result of the controversy, the music public of Vienna

became largely polarized. Billroth, not surprisingly, sided with Brahms and with his stature and dignity—someone called him the stalwart Viking of the North Sea—he delighted in his title of 'Head Brahmin'. On other occasions in softer mood, he styled himself 'a sentimental North Sea herring'. Brahms, it is well known, could sometimes be very uncouth in his manners; and biographers have sometimes contrasted the picture of him—the stocky, sturdy man from Hamburg, who delighted himself that his picture was given in German school geographies as a representative of the Aryan race, now gruff and repelling, now exquisitely sensitive and tender-hearted, now sarcastic and *burschikos*, now charitable in the most stealthy, modest way, incomparably the strongest and worthiest figure in modern Germany—with that of Billroth, the grandson of a famous soprano, of Swedish ancestry and also an emigrant from the north to the south, where he held the esteemed position of surgical professor at the university.

A tragic third figure in this so regrettable atmosphere of animosity was the lovable, unsophisticated but very great symphonic composer, Anton Bruckner, who virtually worshipped Wagner and, as a consequence, became the recipient of some extremely cruel and unjust criticisms from Hanslick.

Billroth and Brahms first met in Zürich in 1866, and some authorities even suggest that Billroth's acceptance of his position at the University of Vienna influenced Brahms to take up residence in that city the following year.

In addition to his surgical writings, Billroth has left us some very lyrical impressions of the composer's works, collected under the simple title of *Briefe*. Many of these letters so impressed Brahms that he quoted them to Clara Schumann; and it is said that the latter even became a little jealous over the friendship. Billroth was the first person to see quite a few of Brahms's new compositions and, at one stage, this afforded him considerable encouragement. After Billroth

38

had praised Brahms's '*Gesang der Parzen*', for instance, the composer wrote back to him:

> You can't imagine how important and precious your approval is to me. One knows what one wanted and how seriously one wanted it. Then one ought to know also what has been achieved; only this one prefers to hear from another person and is glad to believe the kind words. My heartiest thanks for praising my song and thus giving it to me.

Billroth's home in the Alsertrasse in Vienna was evidently a very luxurious one and was situated in a most important quarter of the city. The main university clinic is in that street and opposite it is the Alserkirche, one of the churches in which Schubert sang as a choirboy. It was also the church in which Beethoven's Requiem was held. A further link with the latter composer came to light when Billroth discovered that his home had previously belonged to Dr Johann Peter Frank, one of the doctors who knew Beethoven. In his letter of 27 July 1883 Billroth wrote:

> From some indications it appears that my house was once owned by one of the most famous professors of the period just after Joseph II, Johann Peter Frank. I was satisfied with the probability as far as it went. But Pohl went immediately to the Municipal Council, burrowed in the dusty property-records and elevated the probability to certitude. The wife of the son of the famous Johann Peter Frank, an inconsiderable medical professor, was in her time a famous singer: she sang in 'The Creation' and 'The Seasons' under Haydn. Through this circumstance, Beethoven came to the house where musical evenings were often given in the garden with illuminated scenes from the Italian operas of the time.
>
> The interesting thing for me is that Johann Peter Frank and Beethoven met in my house and that a similar relationship—let us not be arrogant—exists between you and me one hundred years later. Beethoven certainly wandered in this direction. Must not Haydn too have had rehearsals with the abovementioned cantatrice at this house? What a noble triad: Haydn, Beethoven, Brahms!

The two friends used to play piano duets together; and Billroth took the second violin part in some performances of the string quartets. As is well known, both the first and second string quartets Op. 51—one might even call them the Billroth I and Billroth II—in C Minor and A Minor respectively were dedicated to Billroth with the words: '*Seinem Freunde Doctor Theodor Billroth in Wien zugeeignet*'. This was in 1873.

If we now turn to the symphonies, it is interesting to read how Billroth immediately perceived the relationship between the First of Brahms and the Ninth of Beethoven. In one of his letters he wrote:

> Although everything reverberated in the large, empty hall, the effect of the symphony was grandiose. With all the boldness of its construction, nobody can complain of a lack of formal clarity, not even in the first movement which storms along like a hurricane. To me, the motifs of the first movement, despite all their energy and passion, do seem to lack a certain appeal. They are rhythmically too long drawn-out and harmonically too defiant and harsh, although at times there is an intense nostalgia. It is a kind of Faustian overture. The entire first movement can almost be considered an introduction to the whole work. The second movement in E Major which I once played for you, was not interpreted with sufficient delicacy by the orchestra to allow the listener to arrive at the pure sky-blue beauty which inspired its invention. The third movement is simply charming and just beautiful. But the last movement is overwhelming: when the horn solo is heard, every heart vibrates with the strings.

Brahms sent Billroth an arrangement for four hands of his Second Symphony, which was appreciated in the following words:

> I have already completely immersed myself in this piece and it has given me many happy hours. I cannot tell which movement is my favourite: I find each one magnificent in its own way. A cheerful, carefree mood pervades the whole and everything bears the stamp of perfection and of the untroubled outpouring of serene thoughts and warm sentiments.

40

When Billroth first played this symphony himself—some have even given it the appellation of the Pastoral Symphony of Brahms—he exclaimed: 'It is all rippling streams, blue sky, sunshine and cool, green shadows. How beautiful it must be at Pörtschach.' The latter, situated on the Wörthersee, a lake in Austria, was where the work was composed in 1876. In fact, when the composer revisited the village in the following summer, he wrote back to Billroth:

> I only wanted to stay there for a day; and then, as this day was so beautiful, for yet another. But each day was as fine as the last and so I stayed on. If on your journey, you have interrupted your reading to gaze out of the window, you must have seen how all the mountains around the lake are white with snow, while the trees are covered with delicate green.

At that time much of the new chamber music of Brahms had its first hearing in Billroth's fine home on the Alsertrasse. Here the Professor of Surgery insisted on what he called his seignorial rights: he was also an epicure and loved to play the generous host to his friends, especially after the first performance of any new work of Brahms.

After one such celebration, Brahms wrote to him:

> I wish there were two words—for more would not do all—with which to tell you exactly how thankful I am to you for the days that came to an end yesterday afternoon with rehearsals and premiere of the symphony. I do not exactly want to say that my bit of composing is nothing but a troublesome chore, a continuous irritation and that nothing better will come; but you cannot imagine how beautiful and heart-warming it is with a sympathy like yours. In such a moment, one realises that this is the best part of composing and all that is connected with it.

Sad to say, this happy relationship deteriorated in the latter years of the lives of both men and—as is the case so often in human friendships—it was over trivialities and misunderstandings. One of these concerned Billroth's having cut out the dedication to him of the A Minor string quartet and having pasted it under a picture of the composer to frame and hang in his study. When Brahms saw this, he became very upset and said to another acquaintance, Mantyzcewski:

> Can you imagine? Billroth has cut up my quartets. Just think! He who should have known that I love him so well and I would gladly have made a fresh copy of the entire quartet had he so desired. And now he goes ahead and cuts a piece out of it.

Another misunderstanding took place when the music critic Edward Hanslick showed Brahms some letters from Billroth, which were written in sincere praise of his music. One particular remark, however, was not meant to be seen by the composer and, when he did read it, he not surprisingly became very hurt. It was to the effect that he would never quite rid himself of the consequences of a neglected education.

Brahms, deeply wounded, did not speak about it at the time to its writer; but exploded at a later moment when Billroth had invited some friends to dinner. When, at its conclusion, he asked the composer to play some of his works for them, Brahms declined in such a sarcastic and hostile tone of voice that the surgeon never had the courage to invite him again.

A partial rapprochement took place later but the old, cordial friendship was never quite regained. When Billroth died in 1894 one of the pall-bearers at his funeral was the composer, who was to follow him to the grave three years later after the onset of jaundice and death from liver metastases.

9

ANTONIN DVORAK

I should have liked to have found more medical links than I did in the case of that lovable composer who was a contemporary and acquaintance of Brahms, namely Antonin Dvorak (1841-1904). After spending some of his childhood years with his uncle at Zlonice, Dvorak came to study in Prague and there shared rooms with a medical student, Karel Cech, in 1860.

From that time up until his death, almost nothing medical is recorded until he suffered 'a stroke' on a beautiful, fine May day in 1904, when his neighbour living opposite him in Prague, Dr Hnatek, came over to face a medically hopeless situation. One could add that Dvorak kept what were virtually 'surgeon's hours', only attending evening concerts when pressed to do so. This was because he liked to go to bed early so that he could be up before 6 a.m. It was not so that he could be ready for an 8 a.m. operating list in theatre; but in order to play the organ at daily Mass. He did this even during much of the two years he spent in the United States, a stay which inspired several works including probably his best string quartet, as well as his Symphony from the New World.

William His (1831-1904), known to us because of the bundle of nerve-conducting fibres helping to govern the regularity of heartbeat, was the medical expert who identified the earthly remains of the great Johann Sebastian Bach, when they were disinterred in the church yard of the Johanniskirche in Leipzig. Subsequent to this, His had the sculptor, Seffuer, make a bust of the composer based on his anatomical measurements.

10

THE RUSSIAN CONTRIBUTION

Aleksander Porfirevich Borodin (1834-87) can be looked on in some ways as being a direct antithesis to Berlioz in that he was a physician and chemist who regarded music as 'a recreation, a pastime and an avocation that distracts me from my principal activity as a professor'. He thought of himself as just 'a Sunday musician' but even at the age of nine he composed a polka entitled 'Helene'.

At an early age he began to learn the cello and flute and wrote a string trio. As he developed, so did his enthusiasm grow for both chemistry and music. It was said that his rooms became filled not only with musical scores and instruments but also with jars and beakers for his experiments, which included attempts to manufacture fireworks.

Borodin entered the St Petersburg Academy of Medicine in 1850 and very soon began to make a name for himself in chemistry; although his examiners complained that he tended to quote the Bible too much in his answers. At the conclusion of his medical course Borodin did his internship in the military hospital at St Petersburg and there met another future great Russian composer, Moussorgsky. The latter was then a 17-year-old subaltern in the Preobajensky Regiment. At the end of that year Borodin wrote a thesis on the analogy between arsenous and phosphoric acids; and received his M.D. in May 1858. He did not remain long in medical prac-tice as his interests lay more in research, both in physiology and organic chemistry. Between the years 1859 and 1862 he studied these subjects abroad, in Italy, France, Austria and

Germany; and met his future wife, an accomplished pianist, Catherine Protopopoff in Heidelberg.

After he had been made Associate Professor in Physiology and Organic Chemistry at the St Petersburg Academy of Medicine in 1862, Borodin began his important studies on aldehyde-condensation reactions that led to his invention of the Nitrometer to measure the nitrogen content of organic compounds. He discovered the betahydroxybutyric aldehyde Aldol in 1873.

In 1872 Borodin founded the Women's Medical College in St Petersburg and here taught chemistry; and was also a pioneer defender of women's emancipation in Russia. Although he and his wife had no children of their own, they used to foster some of the young children from among the poorer families of the city. From what we read, it would seem that he was an extremely kind person and he lived in 'a constant whirlpool of activity, entangled in a dozen charitable committees, teaching and advising students at the St Petersburg Military Academy and the Women's Medical College, helping out relatives and friends, nursing an ailing wife who had asthma, entertaining and being entertained'.

Nevertheless, in spite of this busy life and the fact that he wrote music more or less as a pastime, Borodin managed to compose two symphonies and left the sketches of a third one. His most famous work of all, the opera 'Prince Igor' with its widely popular and colourful Polovtsian Dances, had not been quite completed at the time of his death; and had to be finished as a joint effort by two other composers, Rimsky-Korsakov and Glazunov. Other well-known compositions include a string quartet and the tone poem 'In the Steppes of Central Asia'. Borodin was a great nationalist in his music, and with his teacher, Balakirev, his friends Rimsky Korsakov, Moussorgsky and Cui, was one of the great Russian Five. He died suddenly in 1887 at a masked ball.

11
GUSTAV MAHLER

Mahler was born on 7 July 1860 at Kalist, Bohemia. Alma
Mahler Werfel, in her biography of her famous husband,
recounts how she first met him in November 1901 at the
home of Professor Zuckerkandl, the great Viennese anat-
omist who has given his name to a layer of fascia around the
kidney. Interestingly enough, that leading contemporary
musicologist and pianist, Paul Badura Skoda, lives in Zucker-
kandlgasse in the suburb of Grinzing in Vienna.

Gustav and Alma Mahler were married on 9 March 1902
in the Karlskirche in Vienna and went to St Petersburg for
their honeymoon. The severe respiratory tract infection that
he contracted on the long journey there is thought by some
to have been in reality an attack of rheumatic fever which
weakened his heart permanently with rheumatic carditis
and atrial fibrillation. Further respiratory tract infections
darkened his first visit to the United States in 1907-8.

When he was suffering from an episode of depression in
about 1909 a neurologist referred Mahler to Sigmund Freud;
but we do not know any details of the psychological con-
sultation.

Mahler returned to America in 1911, making then one of
his renowned remarks, 'Ah, fortissimo at last', when he first
beheld Niagara Falls. Between Christmas 1910 and February
1911 he contracted a further streptococcal infection that led
to sub-acute bacterial endocarditis. This was confirmed by
blood cultures ordered by a New York friend, Dr Joseph
Fränkel. The last concerts of his Philharmonic season had to

Gustav Mahler in the Opera House, Vienna, 1907; *photograph by Moriz Nähe*
From the Society of Friends of Music, Vienna

be cancelled; and he suffered badly from high fevers and rigours on the sea voyage back to Europe. (Another passenger on board the same liner was Busoni, the composer and arranger of Bach's music for piano.)

After the vessel had berthed at Cherbourg, Mahler was taken to the Paris nursing-home of Dr Duprès. Here further blood cultures were made by the bacteriologist, Chantemesse. His comment on the microscopic result—'Just look at these threads—it's like seaweed' certainly gave a vivid scientific description of the proliferating chains of streptococci; but was hardly a kind or wise observation to make to the composer's very worried wife.

As progressive deterioration followed, it was decided to transfer the patient to Vienna, where he was placed under the care of the leading doctor in the city at that time, Professor Chvostek. The latter is best known in medical circles because of Chvostek's sign, namely tapping the seventh cranial nerve in front of the ear to produce a brisk twitch of the muscles of the face when there is tetany, such as after the occasional, accidental removal of the parathyroid glands in operations on the thyroid.

Mahler's last days were complicated by the onset of uraemia with alternating periods of consciousness and unconsciousness. Following his death on 18 May 1911—during a thunderstorm, like that of Beethoven—he was buried in the cemetery at Grinzing.

12

REVERENCE FOR LIFE:
ALBERT SCHWEITZER

Philosopher, theologian, medical missionary, musician and Nobel Prize winner, Albert Schweitzer (1875-1965) must surely rank as one of the most remarkable men of the twentieth century. He was born in Kaisersberg in Upper Alsace in 1875 and, after his theological and philosophical studies had been crowned with a Ph.D. degree in 1899 for his thesis '*Die Religions-philosophie Kants*', he studied music: first in Strasbourg and later in Paris with the composer, Widor.

In 1905 Schweitzer published his first book on Johann Sebastian Bach. It was in French and was followed three years later by an enlarged two-volume German edition. Ernest Newman translated it into English in 1911. In it the author presents not only the full historical and analytical background of the origins of chorales, cantatas and Passion music but also pictures the composer as a deep, religious mystic. He describes Bach as a musician-poet, as a supreme pictorial creator of sound, and follows this with detailed instructions as to how he thinks various works should be played.

On the threshold of what would have been a remarkable career as an organist of world stature, Schweitzer resigned his appointment at Strasbourg University to commence the study of medicine in 1906. He said that he found his inspiration to be a medical missionary from the scriptural parable of Dives and Lazarus, identifying the former with the white man, endowed with all the benefits of cultural science. Lazarus symbolized the African negro, exploited and oppressed and lacking medical treatment for his diseases and pain. The financing of his medical studies was helped by his organ recitals.

After graduation Schweitzer embarked at Bordeaux in March 1913 for Lamberene on the banks of the Ogowe River in what was then French Equatorial Africa. Here he built his first hospital, dispensary and mission; and began his great fight against leprosy, sleeping sickness and other tropical diseases. His music he kept with him by including in his luggage a piano—but it had to be lined with lead as a pre-caution against attacks on its wood by white ants.

Being a German subject, Albert Schweitzer was interned for a short time following the outbreak of the First World War in 1914; and was brought back to Europe to a prison camp in Provence in 1917. All this time, however, was not wasted as he used it to write the first two volumes of his *Kulturphilosophie*, published later in 1923. It is in the second volume of this research work that Schweitzer set out the forc-ible reasons behind his famous and great ethic: 'Reverence for Life'.

His wife, Helene Bresslauk, whom he married in 1922, trained as a nurse so that she could help him in his missionary work. In 1924, when he returned to Africa, he found his hospital a derelict from floods, pestilence and the effects of famine and so decided to move it to a better site two miles upstream, where his small group set to work to build a new and bigger establishment. From that time onwards it grew progressively and an adjacent leper colony was able to be founded.

The proceeds of the Goethe Prize, which was awarded to Schweitzer in 1928, were used for the construction of a complex of buildings, including accommodation for the resident medical staff, visitors to the mission and a hall for lectures and recitals. Being regarded by many as the definitive world authority on the organ works of Johann Sebastian Bach, Schweitzer was being continually asked to make recordings whenever he returned to Europe; and he spoke with some emotion of the great composer being able to help in this way to alleviate the sufferings of his African patients.

His address, *'Das Problem des Friedens'*—'The Problem of Peace'—on being awarded the Nobel Prize in 1952, had a world-wide circulation. In 1955 Queen Elizabeth II bestowed on him the British Order of Merit; and in that same year he broadcast from Oslo his three appeals to the world: *'Friede oder Atomkrieg'*—'Peace or Atomic War'. He died at Lambarene on 4 September 1965 and was buried by his mission.

Schweitzer had an amazing capacity for arduous mental and physical work; and once said that one could burn the candle at both ends, provided that the candle was long enough. Tall and broad-shouldered, he was blessed with an exceptionally strong physique and his facial expressions were, like his character, both forceful and compassionate.

It was also sometimes asserted that he exhibited some shrewdness in his business arrangements and in his administration of his hospital, with an almost patriarchal retention of control of every detail of its workings and management. It may be easy to make such criticisms at a distance but, on the other hand, it may well have been the most practical and efficient management of such pioneering and somewhat unique handling of the situations involved. Furthermore, he would have grown up and studied under the traditional directorship of hospitals by their professors in Europe, especially in Germany. Apart from all his medical work, he wrote on the building and repairing of his favourite musical instrument, the organ.

13
EDWARD ELGAR

I cannot find any very close connection between Medicine and Sir Edward Elgar but, if my fantasy were allowed to soar, I would wonder if Arthur O'Shaughnessy (1844-1881), the Irish poet whose work 'The Music Makers' with its introduction:

> 'We are the music-makers,
>   And we are the dreamers of dreams,
> Wandering by lone sea-breakers,
>   And sitting by desolate streams—
> World-losers and world-forsakers,
>   On whom the pale moon gleams;
> Yet we are the movers and shakers
>   Of the world for ever, it seems.'

and its conclusion:

> 'For each age is a dream that is dying,
>   Or one that is coming to birth'

had any connection with Laurence O'Shaughnessy, the thoracic surgeon who pioneered Coronary Artery By-Pass with his Cardio-Omentopexy in the 1930s? He died in 1940 operating under a pier at Dunkirk and his sister, incidentally, married the writer, George Orwell.

It would, I fear, be mere Irish reverie to link myself with these great men by any other thread than that of a namesake.

INDEX